THE MINDFULNESS COLORING BOOK

D1294393

THE
MINDFULNESS
COLORING
BOOK

ARCTURUS

ARCTURUS

© 2015 Arcturus Holdings Limited

ISBN 978-1-78599-170-7
AD004954NT

Manufactured in China

2 4 6 8 10 9 7 5 3 1

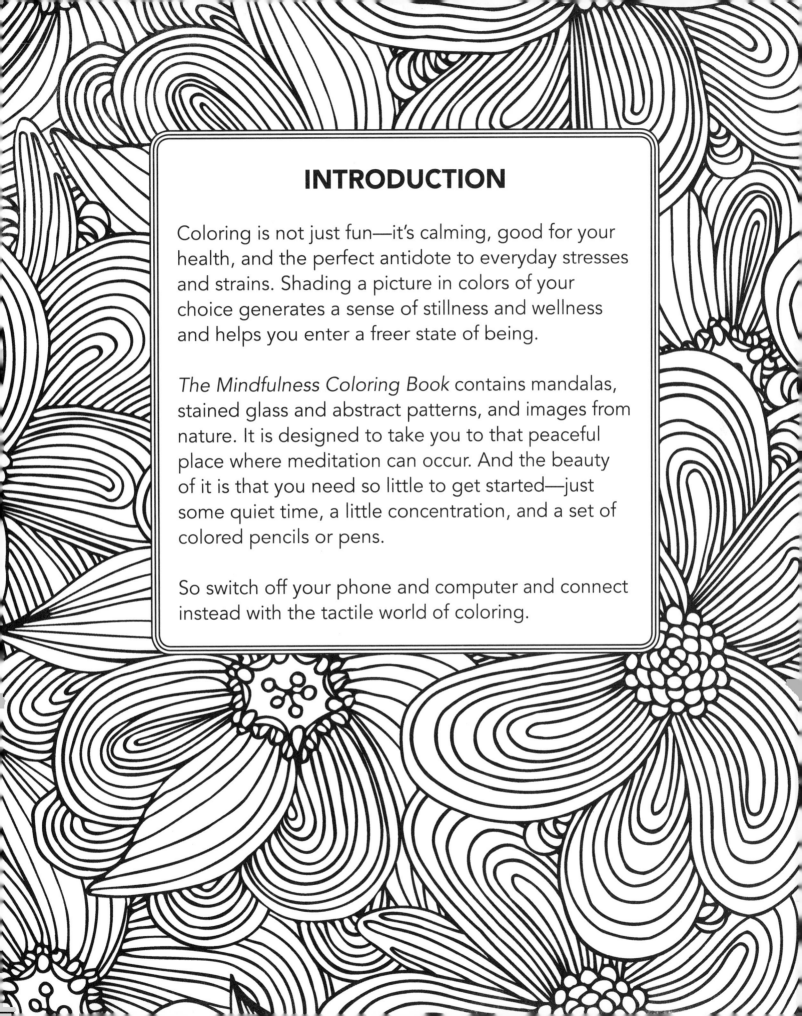

INTRODUCTION

Coloring is not just fun—it's calming, good for your health, and the perfect antidote to everyday stresses and strains. Shading a picture in colors of your choice generates a sense of stillness and wellness and helps you enter a freer state of being.

The Mindfulness Coloring Book contains mandalas, stained glass and abstract patterns, and images from nature. It is designed to take you to that peaceful place where meditation can occur. And the beauty of it is that you need so little to get started—just some quiet time, a little concentration, and a set of colored pencils or pens.

So switch off your phone and computer and connect instead with the tactile world of coloring.

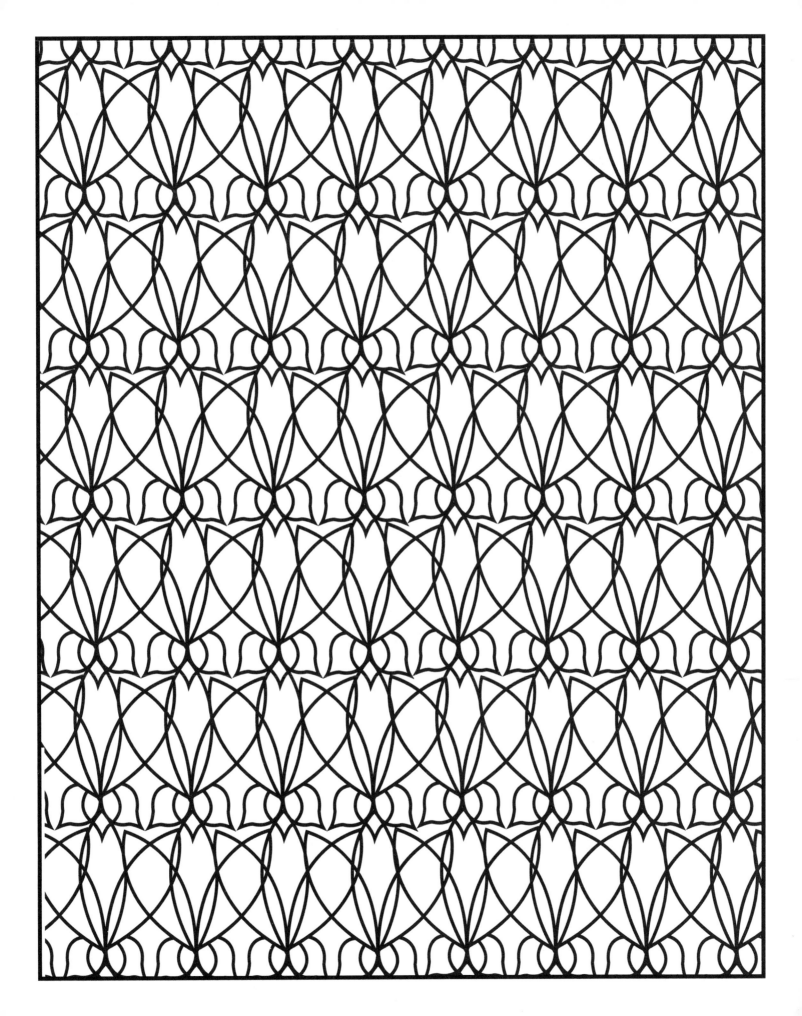

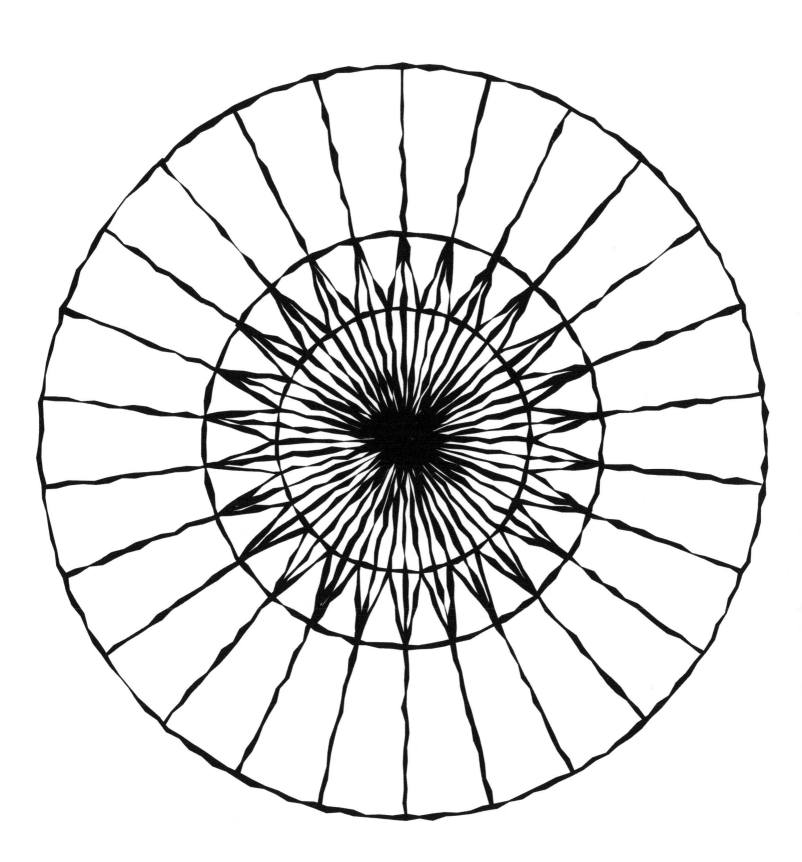

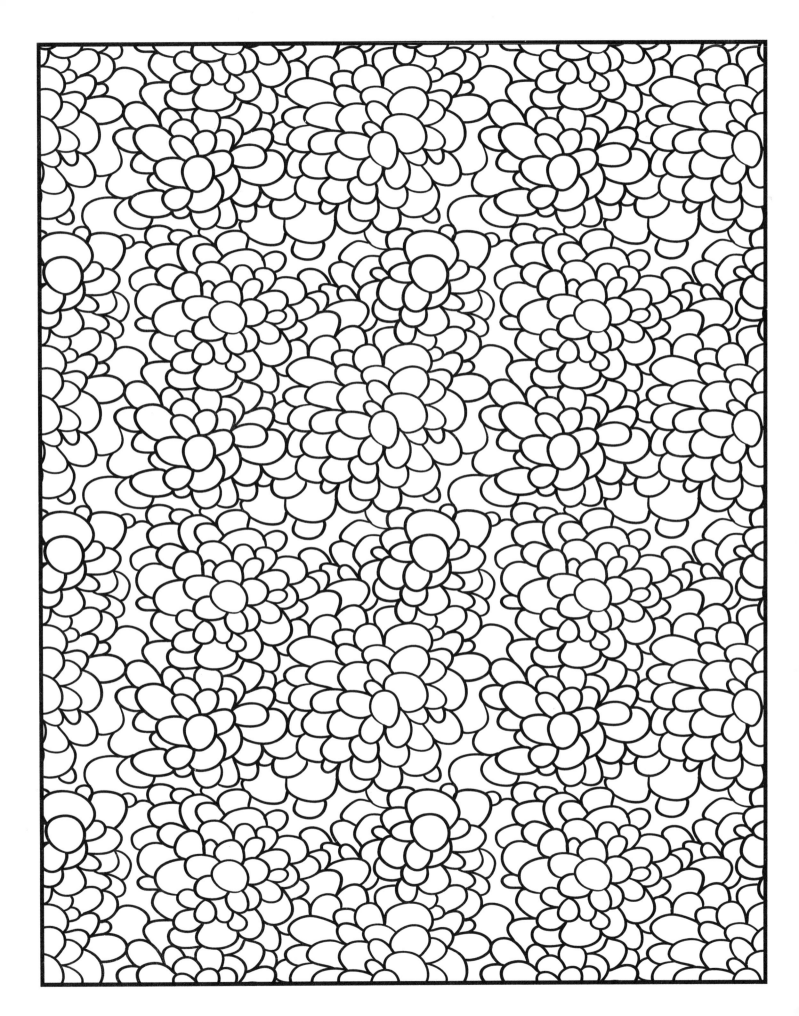

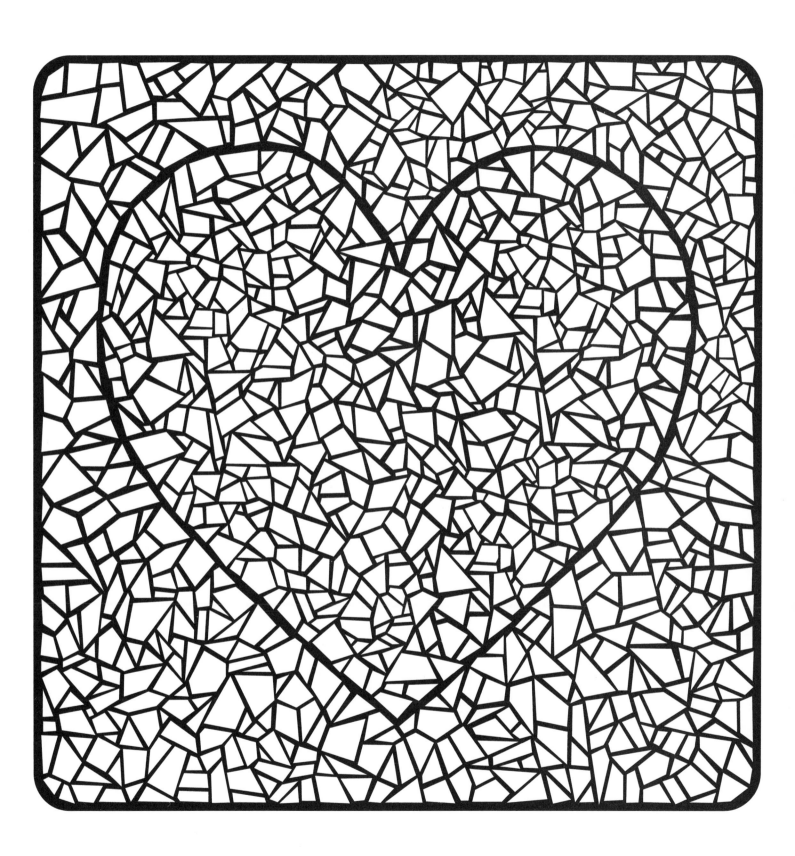

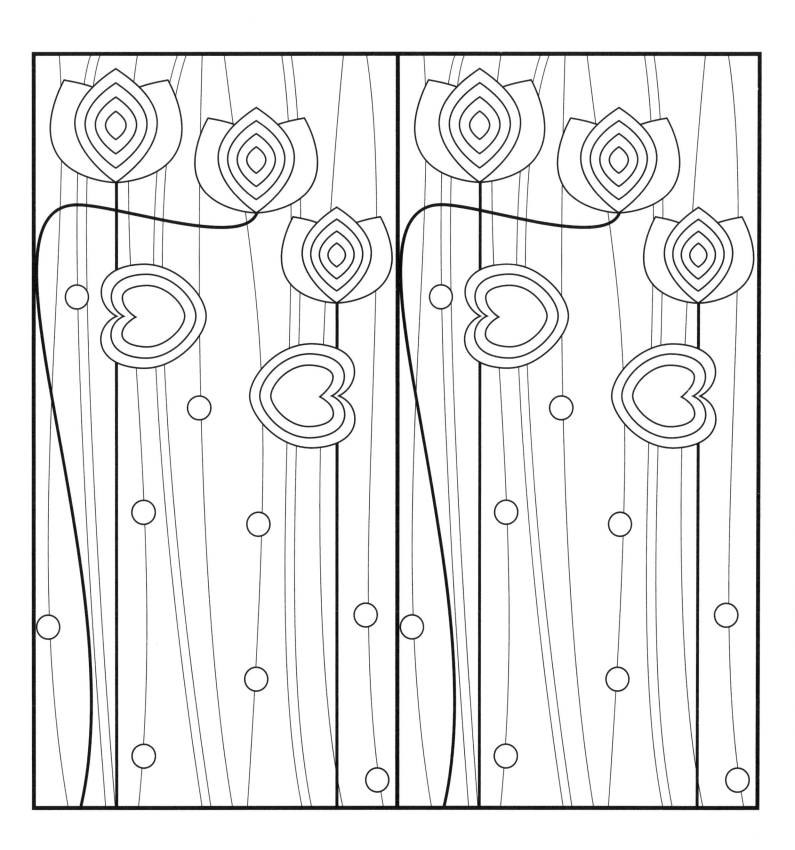

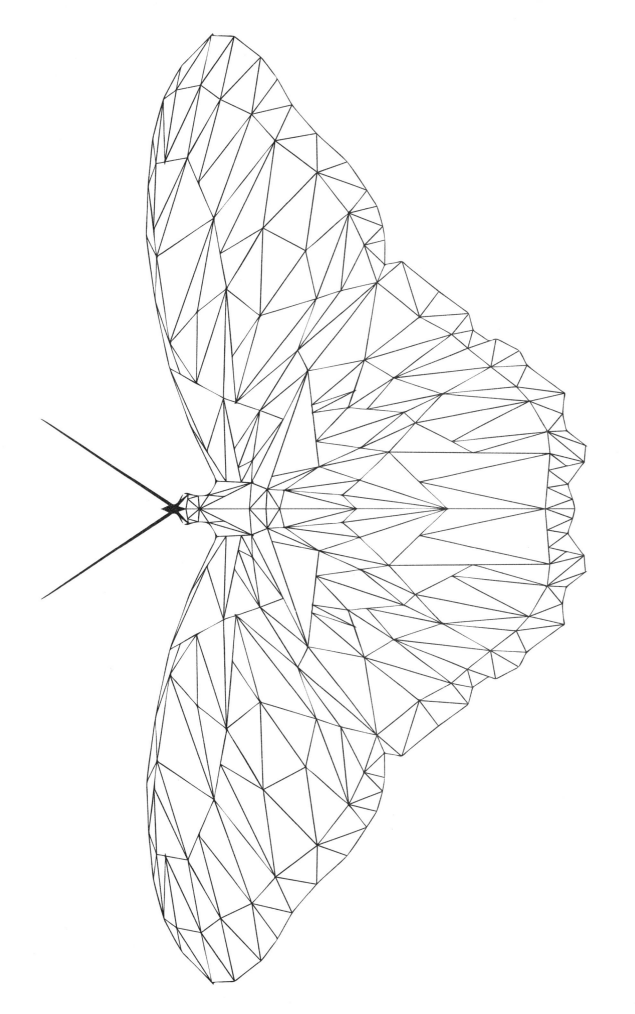

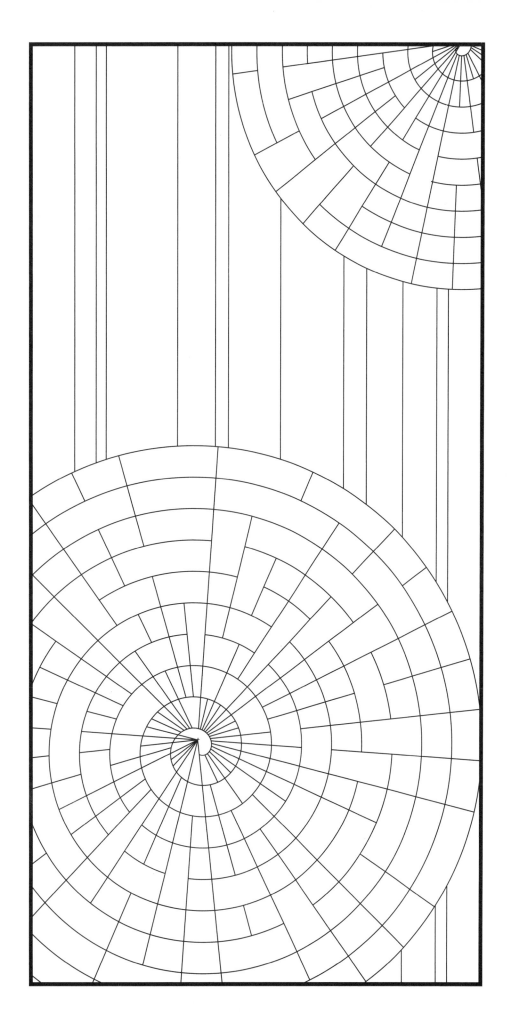

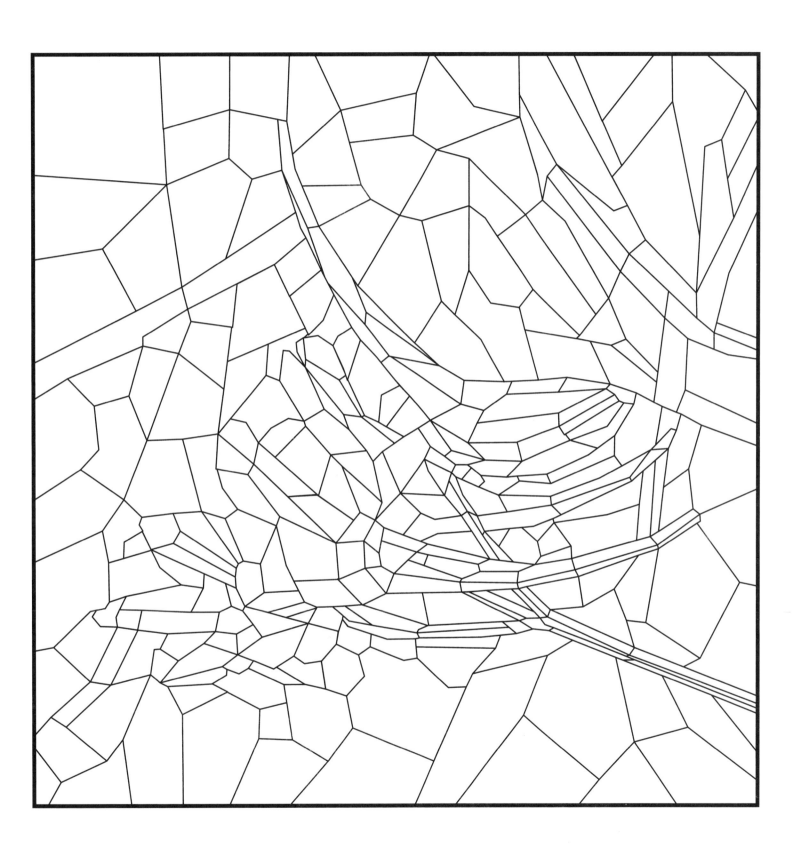

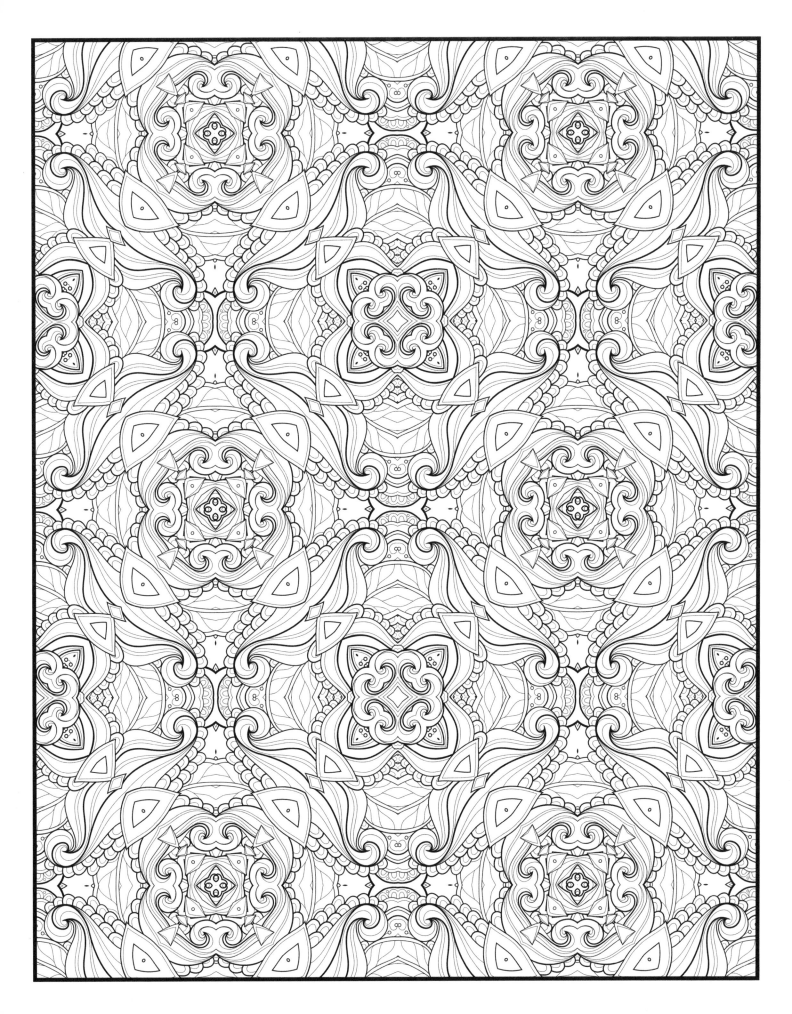

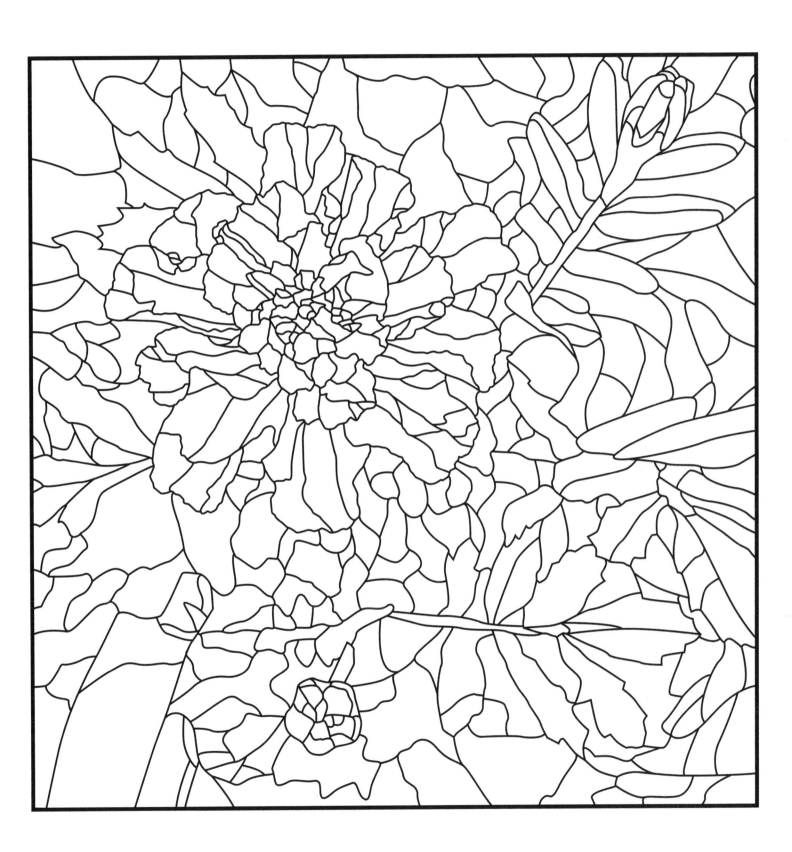

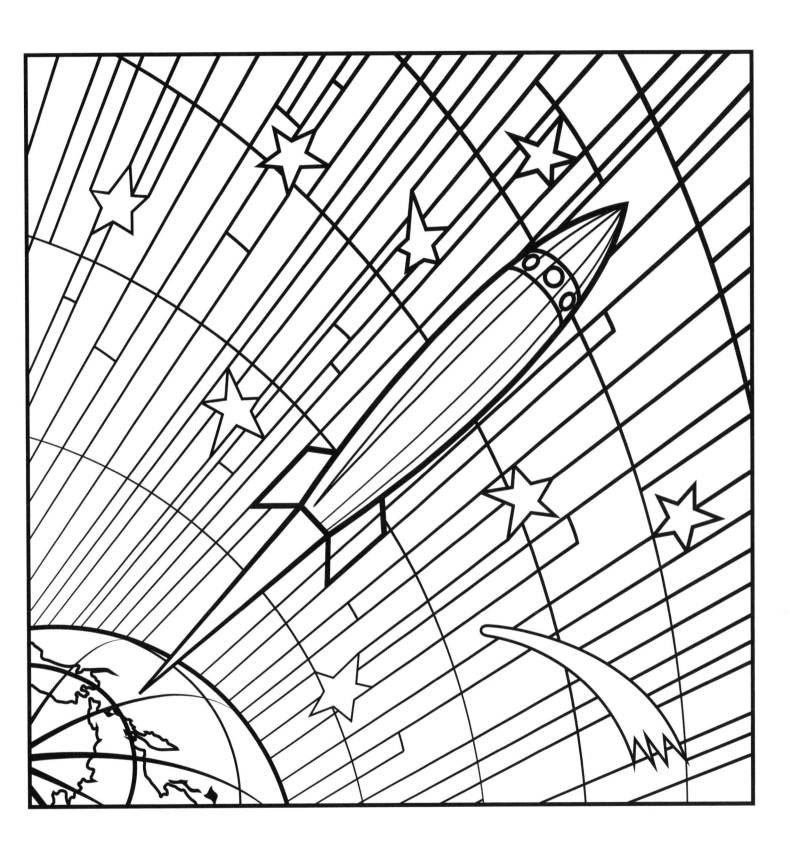

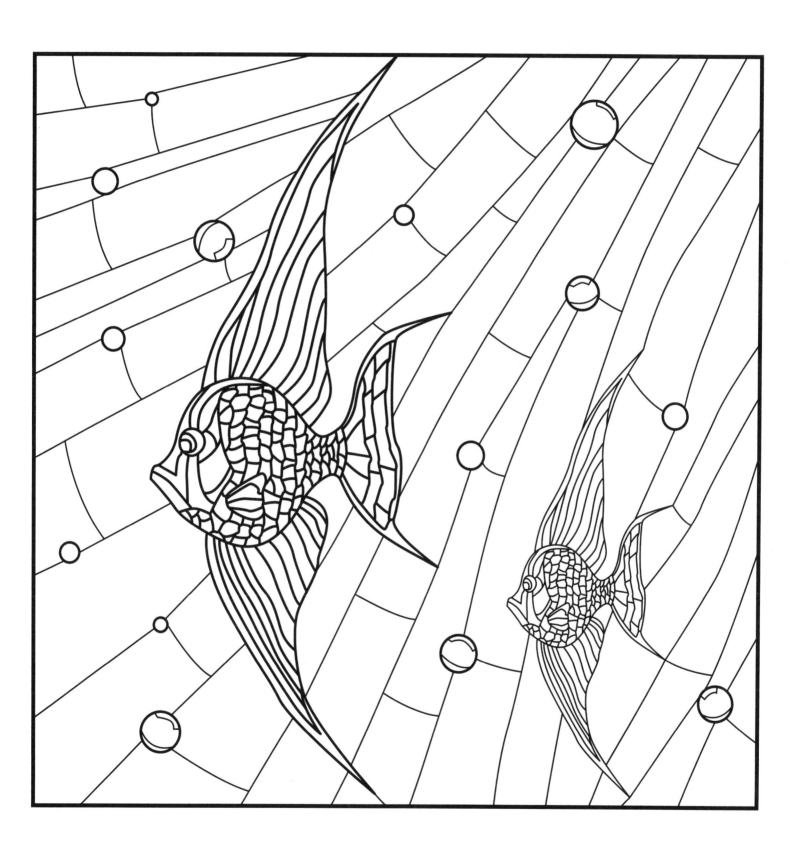